The main characters

Hamlet
The Prince of Denmark. Son of the late king.
Still grieving for his father and filled with
hatred for his uncle.

The ghost of Hamlet's father
The former King of Denmark, also named Hamlet.
He returns from the dead to speak to his son.

Claudius
The devious new King of Denmark.
Prince Hamlet's uncle, brother of
the late king.*

Gertrude
Claudius's new wife, and widow of the late king.
Loyal to Claudius and concerned about her son's
state of mind.

Polonius
Pompous, talkative nobleman.
Advisor and friend to the king.
The father of Laertes and Ophelia.

Laertes
Son of Polonius, brother to Ophelia.
Headstrong and pleasure-seeking, but
deeply devoted to his father and his sister.

Ophelia

Daughter of Polonius. She once believed
Hamlet to be truly in love with her.

Horatio

Hamlet's best friend from university.
Loyal to the prince, whatever he says or does.

Rosencrantz and Guildenstern

Prince Hamlet's childhood friends.
Easily led by Claudius.

*At the time of this story, in some monarchies the eldest brother of a king
(rather than the eldest son) could be chosen to take his place when he died.

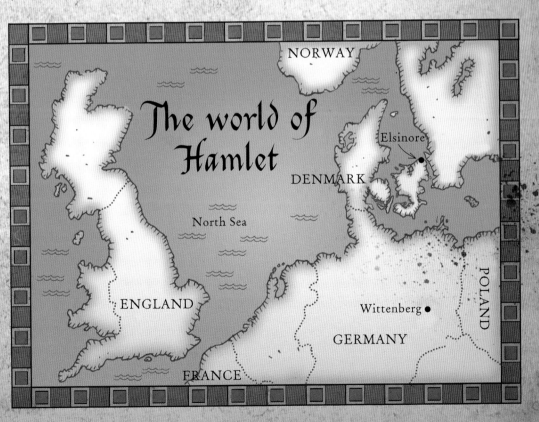

The world of Hamlet

NORWAY

Elsinore

DENMARK

North Sea

ENGLAND

POLAND

Wittenberg

GERMANY

FRANCE

Denmark ~ the late Middle Ages

At Elsinore Castle, home to the Danish royal family, the coronation of Claudius, brother of the late King Hamlet, has just taken place.

Meanwhile, up on the gun terrace of the castle, young sentinel Francisco is eagerly awaiting three guards to relieve him of his watch. Suddenly, a questioning voice calls out to him through the murky mist...

WHO'S THERE?

FRANCISCO DEPARTS, TO BE REPLACED A FEW MOMENTS LATER BY HORATIO AND MARCELLUS...

UT WORD HAS IT THAT **FORTINBRAS'S SON**, WHO SHARES THAT NAME, IS GATHERING N **ARMY** TO **RECOVER** THOSE **LANDS**.

THAT, **I TAKE IT**, IS THE MAIN REASON FOR OUR **PREPARATIONS**.

AT THAT MOMENT, THE GHOST REAPPEARS...

LOOK, IT'S **BACK AGAIN!** I'LL **CHALLENGE** IT, EVEN IF IT **DESTROYS** ME.

SPEAK TO ME! IF YOU KNOW YOUR COUNTRY'S **FATE**, WHICH MIGHT BE **AVOIDED** BY **ADVANCE KNOWLEDGE**, SPEAK!

OR IF, AS SOME SAY, YOU'RE ONE OF THOSE SPIRITS WHO **WALK** IN DEATH, LOOKING FOR BURIED, ILL-GOTTEN TREASURE, **TELL** ME!

SOMEWHERE DOWN BELOW, A COCKEREL CROWS AND THE GHOST TURNS TO GO...

COCK-A-DOODLE-DO!

STOP THE SPIRIT, MARCELLUS!

MARCELLUS AND BARNARDO TRY TO STRIKE THE GHOST, BUT THEIR WEAPONS GO STRAIGHT THROUGH IT...

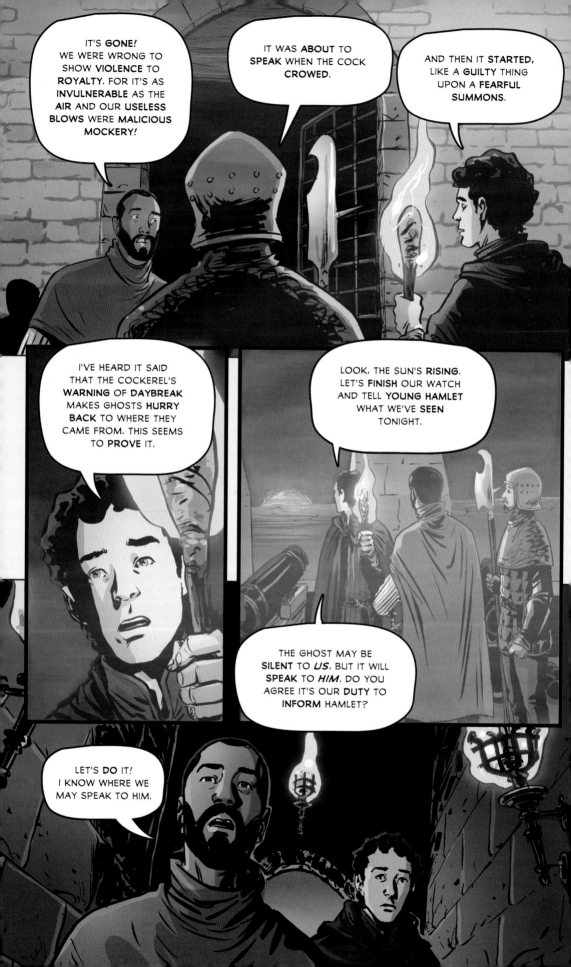

IT CAN COME TO **NO GOOD.** BUT **BREAK** MY **HEART,** FOR I MUST **HOLD MY TONGUE.**

WITHIN A **MONTH,** BEFORE THE **SALTY TEARS** HAD LEFT THE **REDNESS** OF HER **SORE EYES,** SHE **MARRIED.** OH, WHAT WICKED **SPEED** TO **RUSH** INTO **INCEST.**

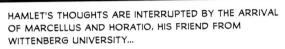

HAMLET'S THOUGHTS ARE INTERRUPTED BY THE ARRIVAL OF MARCELLUS AND HORATIO, HIS FRIEND FROM WITTENBERG UNIVERSITY...

WHAT ARE YOU DOING **AWAY** FROM **WITTENBERG?**

HAIL TO YOUR **LORDSHIP!**

HORATIO!

MY LORD, I CAME TO SEE YOUR **FATHER'S FUNERAL.**

MY **FATHER,** I THINK I CAN **SEE** MY **FATHER...**

OH, **WHERE,** MY LORD?

IN MY **MIND'S EYE,** HORATIO.

MY LORD, I THINK *I* SAW HIM **LAST NIGHT.**

AFTER HORATIO HAS TOLD HAMLET WHAT HE AND THE OTHERS SAW ON THE BATTLEMENTS...

IT'S VERY **STRANGE**.

DID HE LOOK **ANGRY**?

HIS EXPRESSION WAS ONE MORE OF **SORROW** THAN ANGER.

I WISH I'D **BEEN** THERE.

IT WOULD HAV **AMAZED** YOU

I'LL WATCH **TONIGHT**, PERHAPS HE'LL WALK **AGAIN**.

I ASSURE YOU HE **WILL**.

I'LL VISIT YOU UPON THE BATTLEMENTS BETWEEN **ELEVEN** AND **TWELVE**.

HORATIO AND MARCELLUS DEPART.

MY **FATHER'S GHOST**, DRESSED IN ARMOUR! ALL IS **NOT WELL**.

I **WISH** TONIGHT WOULD **COME**. TILL THEN, BE **STILL** MY **SOUL**.

MEANWHILE, LAERTES IS SAYING FAREWELL TO OPHELIA...

SISTER, DON'T **FORGET** TO LET ME **HEAR** FROM YOU WHILE I'M **AWAY**.

DO YOU DOUBT I **WOULD**?

AND REMEMBER, HAMLET'S **LOVE** FOR YOU ISN'T **PERMANENT**, IT'S JUST THE **WHIM** OF A **MINUTE**, NO MORE.

NO **MORE** THAN **THAT**?

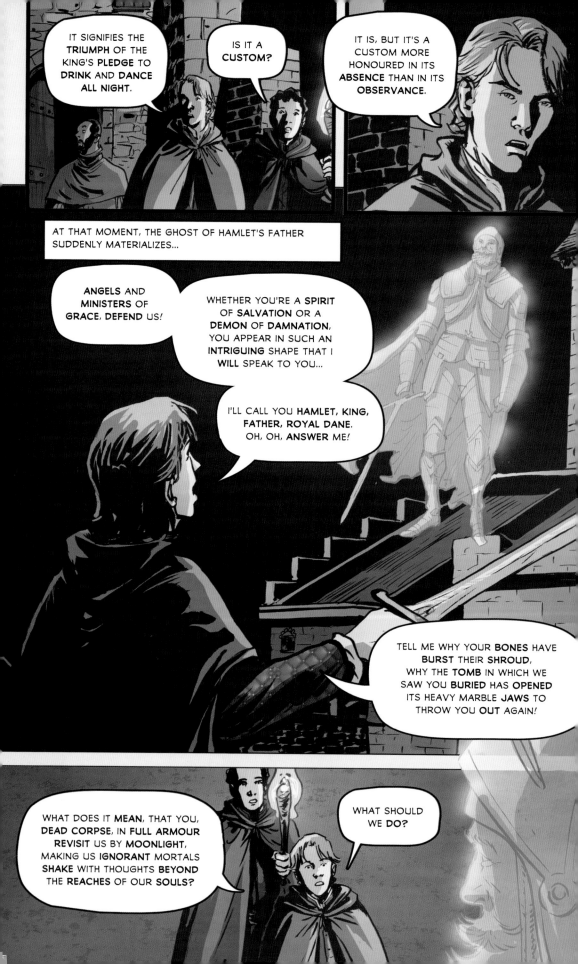

IT **BECKONS** YOU TO **GO AWAY** WITH IT, AS IF IT WANTS TO SPEAK TO YOU **ALONE**.

GO ON, SPIRIT, I'LL **FOLLOW** YOU!

YOU **SHALL NOT GO**, MY LORD.

UNHAND ME GENTLEMEN, OR I'LL MAKE A **GHOST** OF HIM THAT **STOPS** ME!

AS HAMLET FOLLOWS THE GHOST ACROSS THE BATTLEMENTS...

SOMETHING IS **ROTTEN** IN THE STATE OF **DENMARK**.

IF **THAT'S** TRUE, PERHAPS WE SHOULD LET **GOD** DEAL WITH IT?

NO, LET'S **FOLLOW** LORD HAMLET.

REMEMBER YOU? YES, POOR GHOST, WHILE I HAVE MEMORIES IN MY HEAD.

OH, MOST DESTRUCTIVE WOMAN! OH VILLAIN, VILLAIN, SMILING, DAMNED VILLAIN!

A MAN MAY SMILE AND SMILE AND BE A VILLAIN, AT LEAST, I'M SURE HE MAY IN DENMARK.

'ADIEU AND REMEMBER ME.' I SWEAR I WILL.

HORATIO AND MARCELLUS CATCH UP WITH HAMLET...

LORD HAMLET!

WHAT NEWS, MY LORD?

OH, WONDERFUL NEWS!

TELL IT, MY GOOD LORD.

NO, YOU'LL REVEAL IT.

NOT I, MY LORD, BY HEAVEN.

NOR I, MY LORD.

TWO MONTHS PASS. ONE DAY, POLONIUS IS IN HIS CHAMBER WHEN HIS DAUGHTER ENTERS, VISIBLY DISTRESSED...

WHAT'S THE **MATTER,** OPHELIA?

ALAS, MY LORD, I'VE BEEN SO **FRIGHTENED!**

BY **WHAT,** IN THE NAME OF HEAVEN?

AS I WAS SEWING IN MY CHAMBER, LORD HAMLET CAME IN WITH HIS **DOUBLET** ALL **UNBUTTONED** AND HIS **STOCKINGS** HANGING **DOWN** TO HIS **ANKLES.**

HE LOOKED AS **PALE** AS HIS **SHIRT,** WITH HIS KNEES **KNOCKING,** AND A **PITEOUS** EXPRESSION, AS IF HE'D BEEN SENT FROM **HELL.**

WHAT DID HE **SAY?**

HE TOOK ME BY THE **WRIST** AND LOOKED AT MY **FACE** FOR AS LONG AS HE WOULD IF HE WERE **DRAWING** IT...

...HE GAVE A **SIGH** SO SAD THAT IT SEEMED TO **SHATTER** AND **DESTROY** HIM. THEN HE LET ME GO, AND **WALKED OUT,** WITH HIS EYES **FIXED** ON ME **ALL THE WHILE.**

COME WITH **ME.** I WILL GO TO SEE THE **KING.** THIS IS AN **OBSESSIVE** LOVE THAT LEADS MEN TO **DESPERATE** ACTS. HAVE YOU **SPOKEN** TO LORD HAMLET *HARSHLY* LATELY?

NO, MY LORD. BUT I **DENIED** HIM **ACCESS** TO ME, AS YOU **COMMANDED.**

THAT'S MADE HIM **INSANE.** I'M **SORRY** I DIDN'T SEE IT **SOONER.** I THOUGHT HE WASN'T **SERIOUS.**

COME, LET'S GO TO THE **KING.** IT WILL CAUSE **MORE GRIEF** IF WE KEEP IT A **SECRET** THAN IF WE **REVEAL ALL.**

MEANWHILE, IN THE THRONE ROOM, THE KING AND QUEEN ARE GREETING ROSENCRANTZ AND GUILDENSTERN, TWO OF HAMLET'S OLDEST FRIENDS...

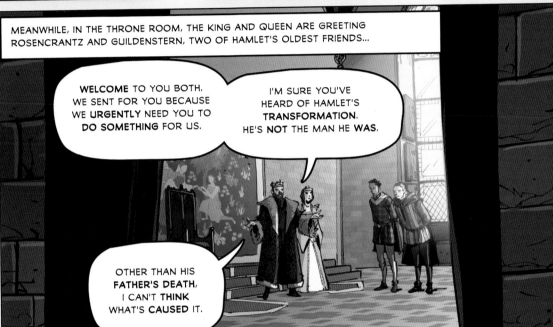

WELCOME TO YOU BOTH. WE SENT FOR YOU BECAUSE WE **URGENTLY** NEED YOU TO **DO SOMETHING** FOR US.

I'M SURE YOU'VE HEARD OF HAMLET'S **TRANSFORMATION.** HE'S **NOT** THE MAN HE **WAS.**

OTHER THAN HIS **FATHER'S DEATH,** I CAN'T **THINK** WHAT'S **CAUSED** IT.

AS YOU **GREW UP** WITH HIM AND ARE OF THE SAME **AGE** AND **TEMPERAMENT,** I THOUGHT THAT IF YOU **SPENT TIME TOGETHER,** HERE AT **COURT,** YOU COULD FIND OUT WHAT'S **WRONG** WITH HIM.

I'M SURE THERE ARE **NO** TWO MEN **LIVING** WHOM HE LIKES **MORE.** IF YOU CAN GIVE US **HOPE** BY YOUR **VISIT,** YOU'LL RECEIVE **THANKS** WORTHY OF A **KING.**

AS OUR **SOVEREIGNS,** BOTH YOUR MAJESTIES COULD *COMMAND* US, IF YOU **WISHED,** RATHER THAN *REQUEST.*

WE BOTH **OBEY,** AND WILL DO OUR **UTMOST** TO **SERVE** YOU AND **CARRY OUT** YOUR **COMMANDS.**

HE'S **FAR** GONE! WHEN I WAS **YOUNG**, I **SUFFERED** FOR **LOVE** LIKE **THIS**. I'LL SPEAK TO HIM AGAIN...

WHAT ARE YOU **READING**, MY LORD?

WORDS, WORDS, WORDS.

IT SAYS HERE THAT OLD MEN HAVE **GREY BEARDS**, WRINKLED **FACES**, LACK WIT AND HAVE **WEAK LEGS**.

ALL OF WHICH I **BELIEVE**, BUT IT'S NOT **DECENT** TO HAVE IT **WRITTEN DOWN** LIKE THIS!

THOUGH THIS BE **MADNESS**, YET THERE IS **METHOD** IN IT.

I'LL GO AND ARRANGE A **MEETING** BETWEEN **HIM** AND MY **DAUGHTER**.

YOU CANNOT **TAKE ANYTHING** FROM ME THAT I WOULD MORE **WILLINGLY PART** WITH, EXCEPT MY **LIFE**...

MY LORD, I MOST HUMBLY **TAKE** MY **LEAVE** OF YOU.

AS POLONIUS HURRIES AWAY, ROSENCRANTZ AND GUILDENSTERN ENTER...

MY **EXCELLENT FRIENDS**! HOW **ARE** YOU BOTH? WHAT'S THE **NEWS**?

NONE, MY LORD EXCEPT THAT THE WORLD'S GROWN **HONEST**.

YOUR NEWS ISN'T TRUE. WHAT HAVE YOU **DONE** TO **DESERVE** BEING SENT TO **PRISON** HERE?

MAN DOESN'T DELIGHT ME.

HA!

NO, NOR **WOMAN** NEITHER, THOUGH BY YOUR **SMILE** YOU SEEM TO **THINK SO.**

MY LORD, THERE WAS **NO SUCH** STUFF IN MY **THOUGHTS.**

WHY DID YOU **LAUGH** WHEN I SAID 'MAN DOESN'T DELIGHT ME'?

I WAS THINKING THAT IF YOU **DON'T** DELIGHT IN MAN, WHAT A **POOR RECEPTION** THE **PLAYERS** WILL RECEIVE FROM YOU. WE **PASSED** THEM ON OUR WAY **HERE.** THEY'RE COMING TO **OFFER** THEIR **SERVICES** TO YOU.

POLONIUS RETURNS...

MOMENTS LATER, THE TROUPE OF ACTORS ARRIVES...

MY LORD, I HAVE **NEWS** TO TELL YOU. THE **PLAYERS** ARE COMING!

I KNOW, I KNOW.

YOU'RE **WELCOME,** WELCOME **ALL!**

MY LORD **POLONIUS,** MAKE SURE THE **PLAYERS** ARE WELL TREATED.

THOSE ACTORS CAN *PRETEND* TO FEEL EMOTION, WITH PALE FACES, TEARFUL EYES AND BROKEN VOICES... AND ALL FOR NOTHING!

YET I, A DULL-SPIRITED RASCAL, CAN SAY *NOTHING* FOR A KING WHO WAS KILLED.

AM I A COWARD? A VILLAIN, A LIAR? I LACK **NERVE**...

...OTHERWISE I WOULD HAVE **FED** EVERY **BIRD OF PREY** WITH THAT BLOODY VILLAIN'S **INSIDES**.

I'VE HEARD THAT **GUILTY** PEOPLE WATCHING A **PLAY** HAVE BEEN SO **STRUCK** BY THE **REALISM** OF THE SCENE THAT THEY'VE **CONFESSED** THEIR **CRIMES**.

FOR MURDER *WILL* SPEAK.

REMORSELESS, TREACHEROUS, LECHEROUS, KINDLESS **VILLAIN**! OH, **VENGEANCE**!

I'LL HAVE THOSE **PLAYERS ACT OUT** SOMETHING LIKE THE **MURDER** OF MY **FATHER**, IN FRONT OF MY **UNCLE**...

...I'LL OBSERVE HIS **FACE**. IF IT TURNS **PALE**, THEN I'LL **KNOW** WHAT **COURSE** TO TAKE.

THE **PLAY'S** THE **THING** WHEREIN I'LL **CATCH** THE **CONSCIENCE** OF THE **KING**!

GOOD **GENTLEMEN**, GO, AND KEEP **ENCOURAGING** HAMLET TO **ENJOY** SUCH **DELIGHTS**.

WE **SHALL**, MY LORD.

SWEET GERTRUDE, **LEAVE US** TOO. I'VE ARRANGED FOR **HAMLET** TO **COME HERE**, SO THAT, SEEMINGLY BY **ACCIDENT**, HE'LL BE **FACE TO FACE** WITH **OPHELIA**.

HER FATHER AND I WILL **SPY** ON THEIR **MEETING** AND **JUDGE** FROM HAMLET'S **BEHAVIOUR** WHETHER HE'S **SUFFERING** FROM **LOVE**.

FOR **YOUR** PART, OPHELIA, I HOPE THAT YOUR **BEAUTY** IS THE **HAPPY CAUSE** OF HAMLET'S **WILDNESS**...

...AND THAT YOUR **VIRTUES** WILL BRING HIM **BACK TO NORMAL** AGAIN.

MADAM, I HOPE THEY **MAY**.

GERTRUDE LEAVES THE ROOM AND POLONIUS INSTRUCTS HIS DAUGHTER...

OPHELIA, SIT OVER **THERE** AND **READ** THIS **BOOK** TO **EMPHASIZE** YOUR **LONELINESS**.

I HEAR HAMLET **COMING**, LET'S **HIDE** MY LORD!

TO DIE, TO SLEEP. TO SLEEP, PERCHANCE TO DREAM. YES, THERE'S THE SNAG. FOR IN THAT SLEEP OF DEATH THE DREAMS THAT MAY COME WHEN WE'VE SHUFFLED OFF THIS MORTAL COIL, MUST MAKE US PAUSE FOR THOUGHT.

IT'S THAT THOUGHT THAT MAKES A LONG LIFE SO CALAMITOUS.

FOR WHO WOULD BEAR THE WHIPS AND SCORNS OF TIME, THE OPPRESSOR'S WRONGS, THE PROUD MAN'S INSULTS, THE PANGS OF UNREQUITED LOVE, THE LAW'S DELAY, THE INSOLENCE OF OFFICIALS, AND THE KICKS THAT PATIENT FOLK RECEIVE FROM THE UNWORTHY, WHEN THEY THEMSELVES MIGHT END IT ALL WITH A DAGGER?

WHO WOULD BEAR THESE BURDENS, TO GRUNT AND SWEAT THROUGH A WEARY LIFE, IF IT WASN'T FOR THE DREAD OF SOMETHING AFTER DEATH, THE UNDISCOVERED COUNTRY FROM WHOSE BORDERS NO TRAVELLER RETURNS? IT BEWILDERS US, AND MAKES US BEAR THOSE PROBLEMS WE HAVE, RATHER THAN FLY TO OTHERS OF WHICH WE KNOW NOTHING.

AND SO CONSCIENCE MAKES COWARDS OF US ALL, AND THE STRONG HUE OF RESOLUTION IS MADE PALE BY THOUGHT, AND ENTERPRISES OF GREAT SUBSTANCE AND IMPORTANCE FADE AWAY INTO INACTION.

GET THEE TO A **NUNNERY.** WHY WOULD YOU BE A **BREEDER** OF **SINNERS?**

I'M QUITE **VIRTUOUS,** YET I COULD ACCUSE **MYSELF** OF **SUCH** THINGS THAT IT WOULD BE **BETTER** HAD I NOT BEEN **BORN.**

I'M VERY **PROUD, REVENGEFUL, AMBITIOUS,** WITH MORE **OFFENCES** AT **MY COMMAND** THAN I HAVE TIME TO **CONSIDER** OR **ACT** UPON.

MEN LIKE MYSELF ARE UTTER **KNAVES.** BELIEVE **NONE** OF US. MAKE YOUR WAY TO A **NUNNERY!**

OH, **HELP** HIM, YOU **SWEET HEAVENS!**

IF YOU **DO MARRY,** I'LL GIVE YOU THIS **ADVICE** AS A WEDDING GIFT – YOU CAN BE AS **PURE** AS **SNOW,** BUT YOU WON'T ESCAPE **SLANDER.** GET THEE TO A NUNNERY, **GO!**

OR, IF YOU **MUST** MARRY, MARRY A **FOOL,** FOR **WISE** MEN KNOW WHAT **MONSTERS** YOU WOMEN MAKE OF THEM.

OH HEAVENLY POWERS, **RESTORE** HIS **SANITY!**

YOU USE **INNOCENCE** AS AN **EXCUSE** FOR **INDECENCY.** GO, I'LL HAVE **NO MORE** OF IT, IT'S MADE ME **MAD.**

I SAY WE'LL HAVE NO MORE **MARRIAGES.** EVERYBODY WHO'S **MARRIED,** EXCEPT FOR ONE, CAN **REMAIN** SO. THE **REST** SHALL **STAY** AS THEY **ARE.**

TO A NUNNERY, GO, AND QUICKLY TOO. **FAREWELL!**

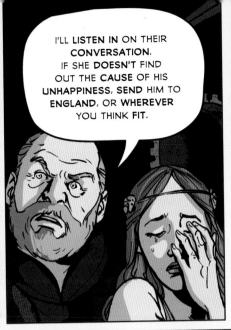

I'LL **LISTEN IN** ON THEIR **CONVERSATION**. IF SHE **DOESN'T** FIND OUT THE **CAUSE** OF HIS **UNHAPPINESS, SEND** HIM TO **ENGLAND**, OR **WHEREVER** YOU THINK **FIT**.

IT SHALL BE **SO**. IF HE **IS** MAD, IT MUST NOT GO **UNWATCHED**.

LATER THAT EVENING, HAMLET INSTRUCTS THE PLAYERS ON THEIR UPCOMING PERFORMANCE...

SPEAK THE **SPEECH** AS I TOLD IT TO YOU, **TRIPPINGLY** ON THE **TONGUE**.

AND DON'T **SAW** THE **AIR** WITH YOUR **HANDS**, BUT BE **GENTLE**. FOR YOU MUST GIVE THE **WHIRLWIND** OF **PASSION** A **SMOOTHNESS**.

I ASSURE YOU WE **SHALL**.

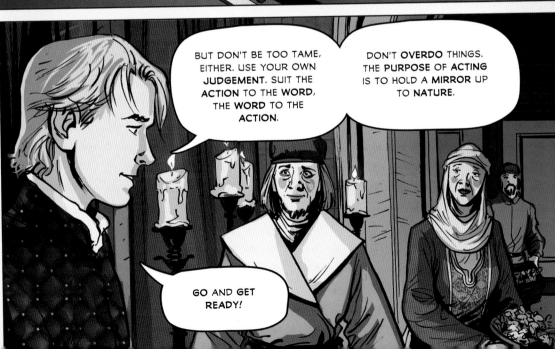

BUT DON'T BE TOO TAME, EITHER. USE YOUR OWN **JUDGEMENT**. SUIT THE **ACTION** TO THE **WORD**, THE **WORD** TO THE **ACTION**.

DON'T **OVERDO** THINGS. THE **PURPOSE** OF **ACTING** IS TO HOLD A **MIRROR** UP TO **NATURE**.

GO AND GET **READY!**

STOP THE PLAY!

CLAUDIUS HURRIES FROM THE ROOM IN DISTRESS, FOLLOWED BY THE REST OF HIS COURT AND THE PLAYERS...

GIVE ME SOME LIGHT. *AWAY!*

...LEAVING HAMLET ALONE WITH HORATIO...

DID YOU **NOTICE** HIM? UPON THE VERY *MENTION* OF **POISONING?**

I CERTAINLY **DID,** MY LORD.

HA! A **RECORDER!** COME, LET'S HAVE SOME **MUSIC!**

AT THAT MOMENT, ROSENCRANTZ AND GUILDENSTERN ENTER...

MY LORD, A **WORD** WITH YOU... THE **KING** HAS **WITHDRAWN** TO HIS **CHAMBER** IN **ANGER.**

THE **QUEEN,** FULL OF **DISTRESS,** HAS SENT ME TO YOU.

SHE WISHES TO **SPEAK** WITH **YOU** IN HER **ROOM** BEFORE YOU GO TO BED.

SIGH. I SHALL **OBEY.** HAVE YOU ANY *FURTHER* BUSINESS WITH ME?

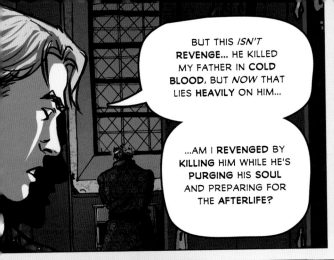

BUT THIS *ISN'T* **REVENGE**... HE KILLED MY FATHER IN **COLD BLOOD**, BUT *NOW* THAT LIES **HEAVILY** ON HIM...

...AM I **REVENGED** BY **KILLING** HIM WHILE HE'S **PURGING** HIS **SOUL** AND PREPARING FOR THE **AFTERLIFE**?

NO.

BACK SWORD, AND KNOW A MORE **SINFUL** OPPORTUNITY...

...WHEN HE'S IN A **DRUNKEN** SLEEP, OR **GAMBLING**, OR **SWEARING** OR IN THE ACT OF **SOMETHING** WITHOUT A **TRACE** OF **SALVATION**.

TAKE HIM **THEN**, SO THAT HIS **SOUL** MAY BE AS **DAMNED** AND **BLACK** AS THE **HELL** IT'S GOING TO.

BUT MY MOTHER'S **WAITING** FOR ME...

MY UNCLE'S **PRAYERS** ONLY PROLONG HIS EVIL **DAYS**.

WHILE HAMLET GOES ON HIS WAY, THE KING EMERGES FROM HIS PRAYERS...

MY **WORDS** FLY UP. MY **THOUGHTS** REMAIN BELOW...

WORDS WITHOUT **THOUGHTS** NEVER TO **HEAVEN** GO.

MEANWHILE, IN THE QUEEN'S ROOM...

HAMLET WILL BE HERE **SHORTLY**, YOUR GRACE.

SPEAK **PLAINLY** TO HIM. TELL HIM HIS **PRANKS** HAVE BEEN **TOO MUCH** TO **BEAR** AND THAT YOU'VE BEEN **PROTECTING** HIM FROM HIS UNCLE'S **ANGER**.

I'LL HIDE **BEHIND** HERE. PLEASE, BE **SEVERE** WITH HIM.

I **PROMISE** I'LL DO AS YOU **SUGGEST**. **WITHDRAW**, I HEAR HIM **COMING**!

MOMENTS LATER...

NOW, MOTHER, WHAT'S THE **MATTER**?

HAMLET, YOU'VE MUCH **OFFENDED** YOUR **FATHER**.

MOTHER, YOU'VE MUCH OFFENDED *MY* FATHER.

COME, COME, YOU **ANSWER** WITH A **LAZY** TONGUE.

GO, GO, YOU **QUESTION** WITH A **WICKED** TONGUE.

HAVE YOU **FORGOTTEN** WHO I AM?

NO, CERTAINLY **NOT**. YOU ARE THE **QUEEN**, YOUR **HUSBAND'S BROTHER'S** WIFE...

...EVEN IF YOU **WEREN'T**, YOU'D STILL BE MY **MOTHER**.

FETCH SOMEONE TO COME TO **TALK** TO YOU...

HAMLET SUDDENLY SEIZES HIS MOTHER...

COME, COME AND **SIT DOWN**. YOU **SHALL NOT BUDGE**...

...YOU'RE **NOT** GOING UNTIL YOU **TAKE A LOOK IN A MIRROR** AT WHAT'S **INSIDE YOU**!

WHAT ARE YOU **DOING**? YOU'RE **NOT** GOING TO **MURDER** ME?

HELP, HELP!

UNABLE TO SEE WHAT'S GOING ON, POLONIUS CRIES OUT...

WHAT'S **HAPPENING**? HELP, **HELP**, **HELP**!

HOW NOW? A RAT?

AS KILLING A KING?

YES, MY LADY, THAT'S WHAT I SAID...

HAMLET SUDDENLY REALIZES THE DEAD MAN IS NOT HIS UNCLE, BUT POLONIUS...

YOU WRETCHED, RASH, INTRUDING FOOL, FAREWELL!

I MISTOOK YOU FOR YOUR SUPERIOR. ACCEPT YOUR FATE – INTERFERING CAN BE DANGEROUS.

DON'T WRING YOUR HANDS, MOTHER. SIT DOWN AND LET ME WRING YOUR HEART, IF IT HASN'T BECOME HARDENED BEYOND ALL FEELING.

WHAT HAVE I DONE, TO MAKE YOU SPEAK AGAINST ME SO HARSHLY?

SUCH AN ACT THAT MAKES MARRIAGE VOWS AS FALSE AS GAMBLERS' PROMISES, SUCH A DEED THAT TEARS THE HEART FROM THE WEDDING CONTRACT.

THIS EARTH LOOKS ON WITH SORROW AND AN ILL FEELING WORTHY OF DOOMSDAY UPON YOUR ACT.

FOR PITY'S SAKE, *WHAT* ACT?

INDEED NOT. INSTEAD YOU'RE LIVING IN THE **STINKING SWEAT** OF A **BED** STEEPED IN **CORRUPTION**, HONEYING D MAKING LOVE OVER THE **NASTY STY...**

OH, SPEAK **NO MORE.** THESE **WORDS** ARE LIKE **DAGGERS** IN MY **EARS. NO MORE,** SWEET HAMLET!

HE'S A **MURDERER** AND A **VILLAIN,** WHO ISN'T WORTH A **FRACTION** OF YOUR **PREVIOUS** HUSBAND.

HE'S A **THIEF** OF THE EMPIRE, WHO **STOLE** THE **CROWN** AND PUT IT IN HIS **POCKET!**

NO MORE!

AT THAT MOMENT, HAMLET SUDDENLY SEES THE GHOST OF HIS FATHER...

SAVE ME, ANGELS, AND HOVER OVER ME WITH YOUR WINGS...

WHAT DO YOU **WANT,** GRACIOUS FIGURE?

HOWEVER THE GHOST IS UNSEEN BY GERTRUDE, WHO CAN ONLY WONDER AT HER SON'S SANITY...

ALAS, HE'S **MAD!**

DO YOU SEE **NOTHING** THERE?

NOTHING **AT ALL.**

DID YOU **HEAR** NOTHING?

NO, **NOTHING** BUT **OURSELVES.**

LOOK HOW HE **WALKS AWAY** – JUST AS MY **FATHER** DID WHEN HE WAS **ALIVE!**

IT'S JUST YOUR **IMAGINATION.** THIS SORT OF **ILLUSION** IS A FEATURE OF **INSANITY.**

INSANITY? MY **PULSE** IS AS **NORMAL** AS YOURS. IT'S NOT **MADNESS** THAT I'VE SPOKEN.

OH HAMLET, YOU'VE **BROKEN** MY **HEART** IN **TWO.**

THROW AWAY THE **LESSER** PART AND YOU'LL LIVE **MORE PURELY** WITH THE **OTHER HALF.**

GOODNIGHT. BUT DON'T GO TO MY **UNCLE'S** BED. REFRAIN **TONIGHT** AND THAT WILL MAKE IT **EASIER** TO DO SO **FROM NOW ON.**

FOR **KILLING** THIS LORD, I **REPENT**. I'LL **DISPOSE** OF HIS **BODY** AND **PAY** FOR THE **DEATH** I GAVE HIM.

I MUST BE **CRUEL**, ONLY TO BE **KIND**.

WHAT SHALL I **DO**?

WHATEVER THE KING DOES TO **TEMPT** YOU, **DON'T REVEAL** THAT I'M NOT **TRULY MAD**, JUST **MAD** IN MY **CUNNING**.

I **PROMISE** YOU, I WON'T BREATHE A **WORD** OF WHAT YOU'VE SAID.

AS YOU **KNOW**, I HAVE TO GO TO **ENGLAND**. *THIS* **MAN** SHALL SET ME PACKING.

I'LL **LUG** THE GUTS AWAY FROM HERE. GOODNIGHT, MOTHER.

MOMENTS AFTER HAMLET HAS DEPARTED WITH POLONIUS'S BODY, THE KING ARRIVES TO FIND HIS QUEEN IN A DISTRESSED STATE...

WHAT, GERTRUDE? HOW IS HAMLET?

YOUR HEAVING **SIGHS** TELL A **STORY**. WHAT **CAUSED** THEM? WHERE'S YOUR **SON**?

AH, MY GOOD LORD, WHAT I HAVE **SEEN** TONIGHT!

MAD AS THE **SEAS** AND THE **WIND** WHEN THEY **FIGHT** EACH OTHER TO DECIDE WHICH IS **MIGHTIER**.

TWO MONTHS PASS. WITH NO WORD FROM HAMLET, CLAUDIUS BELIEVES HE CAN REST EASILY ONCE MORE. THEN, ONE DAY, HORATIO ENTERS GERTRUDE'S CHAMBERS WITH A REQUEST FROM OPHELIA FOR AN AUDIENCE WITH THE QUEEN...

I **WILL NOT** SPEAK WITH HER.

SHE'S **INSISTENT** AND SOMEWHAT **AGITATED**. SHE'S **DESERVING** OF **PITY**.

WHAT DOES SHE **WANT**?

SHE SPEAKS MUCH OF HER **FATHER** AND THAT THE WORLD IS FULL OF **TRICKS**. SHE **HUMS**, **BEATS** HER **CHEST** AND SPEAKS IN AN **UNCLEAR** WAY THAT **DOESN'T** QUITE **MAKE SENSE**.

YET THOSE WHO **HEAR** HER TAKE THEIR **OWN** MEANING FROM HER **WORDS**. HER **NODS** AND **WINKS** ENCOURAGE THOSE FOLK TO BELIEVE THAT THEY'RE **CLOSE** TO THE **TRUTH**.

I'D **BETTER** SPEAK TO HER, FOR SHE MAY PUT **DANGEROUS IDEAS** INTO THE MINDS OF MISCHIEF-MAKERS.

OPHELIA ENTERS WITH A VACANT, DISTANT LOOK IN HER EYES...

WHERE IS THE BEAUTIFUL **QUEEN** OF **DENMARK**?

HOW **ARE** YOU, OPHELIA?

ONLY HIS ENEMIES.

I'LL OPEN MY ARMS WIDE TO HIS FRIENDS AND FEED THEM WITH MY OWN BLOOD.

WHY, NOW YOU SPEAK LIKE A TRUE GENTLEMAN. YOU'LL SOON REALIZE THAT I'M GUILTLESS OF YOUR FATHER'S DEATH AND ONLY GRIEVE FOR HIM.

AT THAT MOMENT, OPHELIA ENTERS, FOLLOWED BY HORATIO. LAERTES IS SHOCKED BY HIS SISTER'S BEWILDERED APPEARANCE...

OH, HEAT, DRY UP MY BRAIN, SALT BURN OUT MY SIGHT! BY HEAVEN, SOMEONE WILL PAY FOR YOUR MADNESS.

OH, ROSE OF MAY, DEAR MAID, KIND SISTER, SWEET OPHELIA! OH, HEAVENS, IS IT POSSIBLE THAT A YOUNG MAID'S WITS SHOULD BE AS MORTAL AS AN OLD MAN'S LIFE?

THEY CARRIED HIM FAR AWAY FROM HERE, HEY NON NONNY, NONNY, HEY NONNY, AND ON HIS GRAVE RAINS MANY A TEAR, FARE YOU WELL, MY DOVE.

IF YOU WERE SANE AND HAD PERSUADED ME TO TAKE REVENGE, YOU COULDN'T HAVE MOVED ME AS MUCH AS YOU'VE JUST DONE.

THIS NONSENSE IS MORE MEANINGFUL THAN SANE TALK.

...BUT, IF **NOT**, WE'LL 'ORK TOGETHER TO PUT YOUR **SOUL** AT **REST**.

LET THIS BE SO. THE **MANNER** OF HIS **DEATH** AND **OBSCURE** BURIAL THAT **LACKED** ANY **FORMAL CEREMONY**, **CRY OUT** FOR **EXPLANATION**.

YOU SHALL **HAVE** IT. AND WHERE THE **OFFENCE** IS, LET THE **GREAT AXE FALL**. PLEASE, COME WITH ME...

...ER THE KING AND LAERTES HAVE GONE, ...AILOR ENTERS...

I'M TOLD YOUR NAME IS **HORATIO**. I HAVE THIS **LETTER** FOR YOU, SIR.

IT COMES FROM THE **AMBASSADOR** THAT WAS BOUND FOR **ENGLAND**.

...TIO EAGERLY READS ...ETTER...

Horatio,

When we'd been at sea for two days, a very warlike pirate ship gave us chase. Finding ourselves too slow to escape, we put up a good fight. In the struggle, I boarded the pirates' vessel at the instant they got clear of our ship, so that I alone became their prisoner. They dealt with me like merciful thieves, but they knew what they were doing: I am to do a good turn for them.

Let the king have the enclosed letters, and come to me as quickly as you can. I have words to speak in your ear that will leave you speechless, yet they aren't strong enough in the circumstances. The sailor who delivered this letter will bring you to me.

Rosencrantz and Guildenstern hold their course for England. I have much to tell you about them. Farewell.

yours,

Hamlet

THEIR CONVERSATION IS INTERRUPTED BY THE ARRIVAL OF A MESSENGER...

I HAVE LETTERS FOR **YOUR MAJESTY** AND THE **QUEEN** FROM **HAMLET.**

FROM *HAMLET?* WHO **BROUGHT** THEM?

SAILORS, MY LORD. THEY WERE PASSED TO ME BY HORATIO.

YOU SHALL **HEAR** THEM, LAERTES...

THE KING DISMISSES THE MESSENGER AND READS OUT THE FIRST LETTER...

'HIGH AND MIGHTY, YOU SHALL KNOW THAT I HAVE RETURNED, DESTITUTE, TO YOUR KINGDOM.

TOMORROW I SHALL ASK TO SEE YOUR KINGLY EYES, WHEN, AFTER BEGGING YOUR PERMISSION, I SHALL RECOUNT THE OCCASIONS OF MY SUDDEN AND EVEN STRANGER RETURN.

HAMLET'

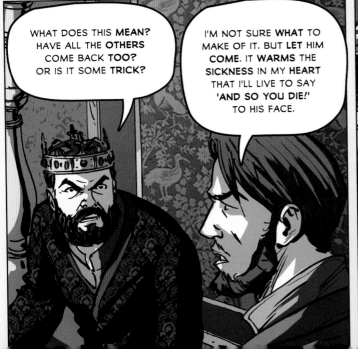

WHAT DOES THIS **MEAN?** HAVE ALL THE **OTHERS** COME BACK **TOO?** OR IS IT SOME **TRICK?**

I'M NOT SURE **WHAT** TO MAKE OF IT. BUT **LET HIM COME. IT WARMS** THE **SICKNESS** IN MY **HEART** THAT I'LL LIVE TO SAY **'AND SO YOU DIE!'** TO HIS FACE.

IN **WHICH CASE,** WILL YOU BE **ADVISED BY ME?**

AS LONG AS YOU **DON'T** ADVISE ME TO MAKE **PEACE** WITH HIM.

IF HE'S **RETURNED** FROM HIS **VOYAGE** AND **NO LONGER** PLANS TO **LEAVE**, I'VE **DEVISED** A **SCHEME** WHICH WILL **LEAD** TO HIS **DOWNFALL**...

...AND THERE'LL BE **NO ONE** TO **BLAME** FOR HIS **DEATH**, SO THAT **EVEN** HIS **MOTHER** WILL **BELIEVE** IT TO BE AN **ACCIDENT**...

YOU MAY HAVE HEARD OF A NORMAN SOLDIER CALLED **LAMORD** WHO GAVE SUCH A **GLOWING REPORT** OF **YOUR FIGHTING SKILLS**, ESPECIALLY WITH A **RAPIER**, THAT HE SAID IT WOULD BE **A SIGHT INDEED** IF **ANYONE** COULD **MATCH** YOU.

HAMLET WAS SO **FILLED** WITH **ENVY** BY THIS REPORT THAT HE **LONGED** FOR YOU TO COME AND **COMPETE** WITH **HIM**.

NOW THAT HAMLET HAS **COME BACK**, WHAT WOULD YOU **DO** TO **PROVE** YOURSELF TO BE YOUR FATHER'S SON IN **ACTIONS**, RATHER THAN **WORDS**?

I'D **CUT** HAMLET'S **THROAT!**

THEN WILL YOU DO THIS... **STAY** IN YOUR **ROOM** – HAMLET WILL KNOW YOU'VE COME HOME – I'LL **ENCOURAGE** PEOPLE TO **PRAISE** YOUR **SWORDSMANSHIP** AND **COMPOUND** THE **FAME** THAT **LAMORD** GAVE YOU...

FINALLY, I'LL BRING YOU TOGETHER AND PLACE A BET ON YOUR DUEL. HAMLET WON'T SUSPECT A THING AND WON'T BOTHER TO EXAMINE THE SWORDS, SO THAT YOU MAY EASILY CHOOSE THE ONE THAT *HASN'T* BEEN BLUNTED.

IN ONE TREACHEROUS THRUST, YOU CAN AVENGE YOUR FATHER!

I'LL DO IT. AND FOR THAT PURPOSE I'LL ADD SOMETHING TO THE BLADE OF MY SWORD...

I BOUGHT AN OINTMENT FROM A TRAVELLING DOCTOR. ONE NEED BUT DIP A KNIFE IN IT, AND WHERE IT SCRATCHES THE SKIN AND DRAWS BLOOD, NO REMEDY IN THE WORLD CAN PREVENT DEATH.

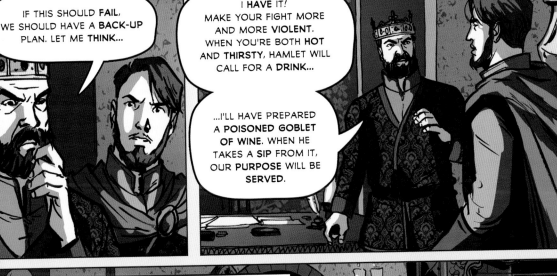

IF THIS SHOULD FAIL, WE SHOULD HAVE A BACK-UP PLAN. LET ME THINK...

I HAVE IT! MAKE YOUR FIGHT MORE AND MORE VIOLENT. WHEN YOU'RE BOTH HOT AND THIRSTY, HAMLET WILL CALL FOR A DRINK...

...I'LL HAVE PREPARED A POISONED GOBLET OF WINE. WHEN HE TAKES A SIP FROM IT, OUR PURPOSE WILL BE SERVED.

GERTRUDE RUSHES IN, VISIBLY DISTRESSED...

WHAT'S WRONG, SWEET QUEEN?

ONE WOE TREADS UPON THE HEELS OF ANOTHER...

YOUR SISTER HAS DROWNED, LAERTES!

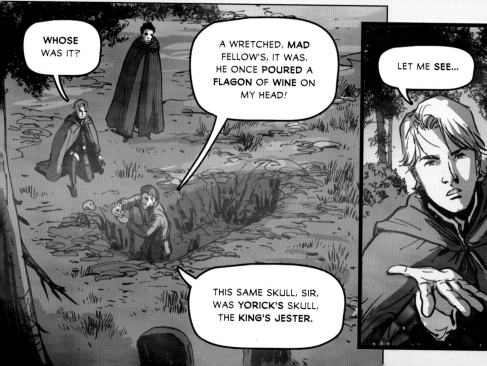

AN **ENTREATY FROM** THE **KING**, STATING THAT IN ORDER TO **ENSURE** LONG-LASTING **PEACE** BETWEEN **ENGLAND** AND **DENMARK**, THE **BEARERS** OF THE **LETTER** SHOULD BE PUT TO **DEATH**, WITHOUT DELAY.

HOW DID YOU MANAGE TO *SEAL* THE **LETTER**?

WELL, **LUCK** WAS ON **MY SIDE** THERE TOO. I HAD MY **FATHER'S ROYAL SIGNET RING** IN MY BAG. I **SEALED** THE **LETTER** WITH IT AND SWAPPED **MY** LETTER WITH THE **OTHER** ONE, WITHOUT **ANYONE** BEING **AWARE** OF IT.

NOW, THE NEXT DAY WAS OUR **SEA BATTLE**, AND YOU **ALREADY** KNOW WHAT HAPPENED **AFTER THAT**...

SO GUILDENSTERN AND ROSENCRANTZ GO TO THEIR **DEATHS!**

WHY, MAN, THEY **KNEW** WHAT THEY WERE **DOING**. THEY'RE **NOT** ON MY CONSCIENCE. THEY **BROUGHT** THEIR **DESTRUCTION** UPON **THEMSELVES**.

WHAT SORT OF A KING *IS* CLAUDIUS?!

DON'T YOU **AGREE** IT'S NOW UP TO **ME** TO REPAY THE **MAN** WHO KILLED MY **FATHER**, SEDUCED MY **MOTHER**, MADE HIMSELF KING TO THWART MY **HOPES** AND AIMED TO TAKE MY LIFE?

WOULDN'T IT BE A **SIN** TO LET THIS **DISEASE** SPREAD ITS EVIL EVEN FURTHER?

CLAUDIUS WILL SOON **HEAR** WHAT'S **HAPPENED** IN ENGLAND.

SHORTLY, **YES**. IN THE **MEANTIME**, I HAVE THE **UPPER HAND** AND A MAN'S **LIFE** IS **BRIEF**.

BUT I'M VERY SORRY THAT I **FORGOT** MYSELF WITH **LAERTES**. FOR I CAN SEE **HIS** CAUSE IS AS STRONG AS **MINE**.

HIS **DISPLAY** OF **GRIEF** STIRRED UP MY **EMOTIONS**.

OSRIC, A YOUNG COURTIER, ENTERS...

WELCOME BACK TO **DENMARK**, YOUR LORDSHIP.

IF YOU'VE FINISHED YOUR **CONVERSATION**, I HAVE A **MESSAGE** FROM HIS **MAJESTY**.

HIS MAJESTY HAS ASKED ME TO TELL YOU THAT HE'S MADE A GREAT **WAGER** ON YOU...

...YOU'LL BE AWARE OF HOW **EXCELLENT** **LAERTES** IS WITH HIS **WEAPON**...

WHICH WEAPON?

RAPIER AND **DAGGER**.

THAT'S *TWO* WEAPONS, BUT **GO ON**...

THE KING HAS WAGERED **SIX** OF HIS **BARBARY HORSES** AGAINST LAERTES'S **SIX FRENCH RAPIERS** AND **DAGGERS**.

I'LL **COMPETE** WITH YOU, WITH **NO ILL FEELING.**

GIVE US THE **SWORDS,** COME ON.

COME, ONE FOR **ME.**

GIVE THEM THE **SWORDS,** YOUNG OSRIC.

AS THE KING PREDICTED, HAMLET PICKS THE FIRST SWORD THAT COMES TO HAND...

THIS ONE WILL DO FOR **ME.** THEY'RE ALL THE **SAME LENGTH** AREN'T THEY?

...WHILST LAERTES IS CAREFUL TO PICK THE ONLY SHARP SWORD, WHICH HE HAS PREVIOUSLY SMEARED WITH POISON...

PUT THE **CUP** AND **WINE** UPON THAT **TABLE.**

IF HAMLET MAKES THE **FIRST** OR **SECOND** HIT, OR REPAYS LAERTES WITH A HIT IN THE **THIRD** ROUND, I'LL **DRINK** TO HAMLET'S **SUPERIORITY** AND **THROW** A VALUABLE **PEARL** IN THE **CUP.**

COME, **BEGIN!** JUDGES – KEEP A **WARY EYE** ON THEM.

OUR **SON** SHALL **WIN**.

HE'S OUT OF **BREATH**...

HERE'S A **NAPKIN**, MOP YOUR **BROW**.

AS THE QUEEN APPROACHES HAMLET, SHE PICKS UP THE CUP OF WINE, UNAWARE OF ITS DEADLY CONTENTS...

I **TOAST** YOUR **GOOD FORTUNE**, HAMLET!

GERTRUDE, DO NOT DRINK!

I **WILL** MY LORD, PLEASE **EXCUSE** ME...

I **DARE NOT** DRINK YET, MADAM. I WILL **SHORTLY**.

COME, LET ME **WIPE** YOUR **FACE**.

WHILE HAMLET IS BEING ATTENDED TO BY THE QUEEN...

MY LORD, I'LL **HIT** HIM **NOW**...

I **DOUBT** IT.

...AND **YET** IT'S **ALMOST** AGAINST MY **CONSCIENCE!**

AS THE TWO MEN TUSSLE, THEY DROP THEIR SWORDS...

...AND, WITHOUT REALIZING, PICK UP EACH OTHER'S WEAPON...

SECONDS LATER, HAMLET STRIKES LAERTES WITH HIS OWN SWORD...

AGH!

OHHHH!

LOOK TO THE **QUEEN!**

BOTH MEN ARE **WOUNDED!**

ARE YOU **ALL** RIGHT, MY LORD?

ARE YOU **HURT,** LAERTES?

AS THE POISON BEGINS TO TAKE EFFECT ON HIM, LAERTES REALIZES WHAT HAS HAPPENED...

WHY, OSRIC, I'M **JUSTLY KILLED** BY MY **OWN** TREACHERY!

ENRAGED AND DESPERATE TO ENSURE CLAUDIUS'S DEATH, HAMLET FORCES THE KING TO DRINK THE REMAINS OF THE POISONED WINE...

THE END

The Story of Hamlet

The tragedy *Hamlet* was written in the 17th century by William Shakespeare, generally considered to be one of the greatest writers of all time.

Shakespeare was baptised in Stratford-upon-Avon, England, on 26 April, 1564. The son of John Shakespeare, a councillor and glove-maker, and Mary Arden, a wealthy landowner's daughter, he was educated at the local King Edward VI grammar school. At the age of 18, he married 26 year-old Anne Hathaway. Six months later, the couple had a daughter, Susanna, and two years after that, twins Hamnet and Judith were born, though Hamnet died at the age of just 11.

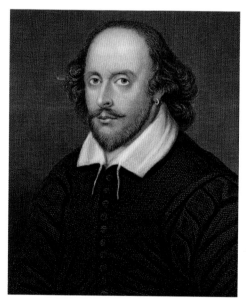

William Shakespeare

It's not certain when Shakespeare began writing, but his earliest historical plays, such as *Richard III* and *Henry VI* (*parts 1-3*), were being staged in London by 1592, when Shakespeare was 28 years old.

From 1594, his work was performed solely by the Lord Chamberlain's Men acting troupe, a company owned by a group of performers including Shakespeare himself. He appeared in his own plays as well as those of other authors.

In 1599, the company built their own theatre, *The Globe*, on the south bank of the River Thames in London. By now, Shakespeare was a wealthy man. He was able to buy New Place, the largest house in the borough of Stratford, from where he travelled back and forth on a regular basis to rented rooms in London.

The original *Globe* theatre

The early part of Shakespeare's career was dominated by romantic comedies and historical dramas. By the early 17th century, he was writing more and more tragedies, including *Hamlet* which was written sometime between 1599 and 1602.

The roots of Shakespeare's *Hamlet* lie in the medieval Scandinavian legend of Prince Amleth, son of King Horvendill, which contains a number of the plot elements in the play.

Another possible source could be an earlier version of the play written around 1587 and staged at Shoreditch, London. Little is known about the piece, however, as no manuscript of the play has survived. Some scholars credit this work to English playwright Thomas Kyd (1558-1594). Others historians believe that William Shakespeare himself may have written the play and that it was in fact an early version of *Hamlet*.

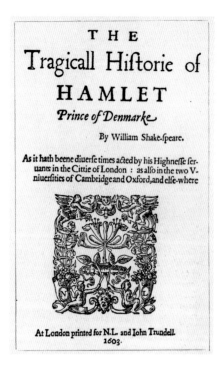

THE
Tragicall Hiftorie of
HAMLET
Prince of Denmarke
By William Shake-fpeare.

As it hath beene diuerfe times acted by his Highneffe fer-
uants in the Cittie of London : as alfo in the two V-
niuerfities of Cambridge and Oxford, and elfe-where

At London printed for N.L. and Iohn Trundell.
1603.

This title page of the first printed edition of *Hamlet* from 1603 refers to the fact that the play had been performed in London, and at Oxford and Cambridge universities.

The title of the play coincides with the name of Shakespeare's own son, Hamnet ('Hamlet' was an alternative spelling).

Hamlet is Shakespeare's longest play, at just over 4,000 lines. If performed in full, it can run for over four hours. Because of this, most productions tend to trim certain scenes or even omit them entirely.

Shakespeare wrote the part of Hamlet for Richard Burbage, the leading tragic actor in the Lord Chamberlain's Men. Since that time, the character of Hamlet has become one of the most iconic parts in theatre and the play is among Shakespeare's most performed works. Memorable stage interpretations include those of Victorian actor-manager Henry Irving in the 1870s,

John Gielgud, who played the role over 500 times in the 1930s, Richard Burton, who enjoyed a record-breaking run in the United States from 1964 to 1965 and Ian Charleson, whose 1989 performance was critically acclaimed.

18th-century Welsh actress Sarah Siddons is the first woman known to have played Hamlet. Sarah Bernhardt took the role on stage in 1899, a short extract of which survives on film.

Laurence Olivier played the role in the Oscar-winning film of 1948, and a famous Russian movie was made in 1964. Kenneth Branagh directed and starred in a 1996 film version which retained all Shakespeare's dialogue.

After 1610, Shakespeare's professional output slowed down. His last three plays were written in collaboration with the up-and-coming writer John Fletcher. Fletcher succeeded him as the chief playwright of the King's Men. This was the new name for the Lord Chamberlain's Men, after they received royal patronage from King James I in 1603.

William Shakespeare died of unknown causes on 23 April, 1616, at the age of 52, and was buried in Holy Trinity Church in Stratford. His life and work are commemorated in numerous memorials, including Poet's Corner in Westminster Abbey, London.

Shakespeare's memorial in Westminster Abbey

Russell Punter was born in Bedfordshire, England. From an early age he enjoyed writing and illustrating his own stories. He trained as a graphic designer at art college in West Sussex before entering publishing in 1987. He has written over sixty books for children, ranging from original stories to adaptations of classic novels.

Valentino Forlini was born in Cremona, Italy, in 1970. He has been a comic book artist since 1996 and has worked for major publishers in Italy such as Star Comics on *Samuel Sand*, *Lazarus Ledd* and *Goccianera*, Eura on *John Doe* and Sergio Bonelli Editore on *Nathan Never* and *Le Storie*. Over the years, he has worked for the Walt Disney Company on various projects including *Chicken Little*, *The Wild*, *Lilo and Stich*, *Meet the Robinsons*, *Pirates of the Caribbean*, *Cars*, *Toy Story* and *Power Rangers*. Valentino is also a storyboard artist and has worked on several TV cartoon series including *Team Galaxy*, *MBC*, *Famous Five*, *Spiez*, *Gormiti* and *Stefi's World*.

Romina Denti is a freelance author and illustrator. Since the early 1990s, she has worked as a colourist and background artist with prestigious publishers and TV production companies. Some of the publications she has worked on include *13 Chambers*, *Singularity* and *Le fauteuil du diable*. She has also contributed to the cartoon TV series *Gladiators*, *Ants*, *Dinofroz*, *Spike Team*, *Waterloo*, and *Nefertine on the Nile*.

Dr. Paul Edmondson is Head of Research for The Shakespeare Birthplace Trust and an Honorary Fellow of The Shakespeare Institute, University of Birmingham. He has written many books and articles about Shakespeare, including his introduction for the general reader *Shakespeare: Ideas in Profile*. He has also published a collection of poems inspired by Shakespeare, *Destination Shakespeare* (which includes a poem based on *Hamlet*), and is a trustee of The British Shakespeare Association.

Mike Collins has been creating comics for over 25 years. Starting on *Spider-Man* and *Transformers* for Marvel UK, he has also worked for DC, 2000AD and a host of other publishers. In that time he's written or drawn almost all the major characters for each company – *Wonder Woman*, *Batman*, *Superman*, *Flash*, *Teen Titans*, *X-Men*, *Captain Britain*, *Judge Dredd*, *Sláine*, *Rogue Trooper*, *Darkstars*, *Peter Cannon: Thunderbolt* and more. He currently draws a series of noir crime fiction graphic novels, *Varg Veum*. He also provides storyboards for TV and movies, including *Doctor Who*, *Sherlock*, *Igam Ogam*, *Claude*, *Hana's Helpline* and *Horrid Henry*.

Page 108: Portrait of William Shakespeare – Photo by Stock Montage/Getty Images
Page 109: Illustration of *The Globe Theatre* – Photo by Ann Ronan Pictures/Print Collector/Getty Images
Page 110: Title page of printed edition of *Hamlet* – © Lebrecht Music & Arts / Alamy Stock Photo
Page 111: Shakespeare's memorial – Photo by Prisma Bildagentur/Universal Images Group via Getty Images

First published in 2020 by Usborne Publishing Ltd.,
Usborne House, 83-85 Saffron Hill, London EC1N 8RT, England. Usborne.com
Copyright © 2020 Usborne Publishing Ltd.